I Go to Jesus

By Carissa Douglas

A special thank you to Regina Doman and Andrew Schmiedicke
for your guidance, insight, and encouragement;
to Pam Damianopoulos for bringing everything together so beautifully;
and to my Patrick, my very own personal Saint Joseph.

Published by Scepter Publishers, Inc.
info@scepterpublishers.org
www.scepterpublishers.org
800-322-8773
New York

Design and Layout by Rose Design
Author family photo credit: Richard Tracey

Library of Congress Cataloging-in-Publication Data in progress

ISBN: 978-1-59417-304-2 (pbk)
ISBN: 978-1-59417-307-3 (ebook)

For inquiries contact: littledouglings@gmail.com
www.littledouglings.com

Printed in the United States of America

Dedicated to my little ones, Liam, Christian, Allora,
Mary, Angelica, Serena, Joachim, Kiara, James, Jacinta, and Callista.
We are so blessed to be able to talk to Jesus anytime, anywhere,
but I pray you will always remember what it gift it is to have Jesus
present to us in the most excellent way in the Holy Eucharist
and that you will encounter Him there often.

When I go to church
I see people in prayer.
They come to see Jesus,
they know that He's there.

I see the tabernacle and I genuflect—
it's a small way I can show my respect.
Our tabernacle is silver and gold,
it's bright and it's shiny and I know that it holds
a wondrous treasure that just looks like bread,
but it isn't bread really, it's Jesus instead.

With Jesus before me, my heart is at ease
like the warmth of a sunrise, the song of a breeze.
I tell Him everything, knowing He'll hear,
His eyes fixed on me, His arms ever near,
ready to hold me and say, "It's okay.
I'm here for you always and I am the Way."

So when Mass is over, I like to stay
and spend time with Jesus to thank Him and pray.
Dad taught me that Jesus is here in the Host
so I come to Him when I need Him the most.

When people are teasing,
when friends aren't so friendly,
when words are so mean
that they hurt and offend me;
when I feel unwanted, upset, and alone,
when I don't fit in and I want to run home,

my mother tells me, "Those words are not true.
Just know you are special and that I love you.
Let's go and see Jesus. Our church is so near.
Go in and see Him, He'll wipe every tear."

So I go to Jesus whenever my heart aches
from feeling left out. And that's when my Lord takes
the hurt and the pain of feeling alone;
He fills me with peace and calls me His own.
Here in His presence no words can defeat me
for He is here with me and loves me completely.

And at Mass I feel close to Him 'cause I believe
that in Holy Communion it's Him I receive.

The baby is pulling my piggly-pig tails,
then he pinches my arm and I let out a wail.
How can I try to be "full of grace"
when stinky, socked feet are too close to my face?
My book's being torn by my troublesome brother,
my stuff's being swiped by one sister or other!

Dad's words, "Stop that now!" come all but too late
'cause I'm already mad, in a crazed, crazy state!
I turn red and explode with a huge Tarzan shout . . .
then realize it's me who needs a "time out."

So I go to Jesus and know I'll find rest,
'cause time spent with Him is time that is blessed.
He quiets my heart, whispers to my soul,
He knows that I'm sorry and tells me, "Let go."
Somehow my anger, my problems and troubles
start popping away like big bath time bubbles.

And before I know it, I'm ready to face
those wild kids at home invading my space.
I tell Him, "Goodbye. I'll come back again,"
and the peace that He gives me I bring back to them.

When drawings are horrible right from the start—
my pictures look more like they're paint blobs than art!—
I spill things and break stuff and everything's wrong
and I want to give up 'cause I'm just not that strong.

Mom hugs me and tells me it all will work out
and not to give in to those feelings of doubt.
"Let's go see Jesus and He'll help you fight
the feeling that you can't do anything right.
When looking for hope, the best place to begin
is in Our Lord's presence, so let's go to Him."

Then I go to Him and my head is hung low.
I try not to cry as I reach the front row.
I quietly kneel and pray, "Jesus, help me.
I'm feeling so hopeless and I just can't see
how you could love me when I can't do stuff
and when I believe that I'm not good enough.

I feel His gaze on me. He says, "Let me free
your heart from the doubts and anxiety.
My Child, please remember how much I love you
for all that you are, not what you can do."
My heart fills with joy, I thank Him and then
I tell Him I can't wait to see Him again.

So sometimes . . .

I go to Jesus when nothing is wrong,
when I just want to talk or to sing Him a song.
Sometimes I just want to share some good news
or even show Him my new pair of shoes.
I can simply be with Him, knowing He's there;
I'm held in His love, as at Him I stare.

I know He's here 'cause He said He would be.
Though His face in the Host I may not see,
His invisible arms extend to my heart,
His promise to stay with me, never to part.
Here in this church, fulfilled in this Host,
I go to Him whom I love the most.

So when someone looks sad 'cause they've had a bad day,
I put my arm around them and quietly say,
"You should go to Jesus, just like I do.
He loves when we visit. He's waiting for you."